MY SNEEZE

My Sneezes Are Perfect

Rakhshan Rizwan
with Yusuf Samee

illustrated by
Benjamin Phillips

THE EMMA PRESS

First published in the UK in 2021 by the Emma Press Ltd.
Poems © Rakhshan Rizwan and Yusuf Samee 2021.
Illustrations © Benjamin Phillips 2021.

The right of Rakhshan Rizwan, Yusuf Samee and Benjamin
Phillips to be identified as the creators of this work has
been asserted in accordance with the Copyright, Designs
and Patents Act 1988.

ISBN 978-1-912915-68-2

A CIP catalogue record of this book is available
from the British Library.

Printed and bound in the UK by Imprint Digital, Exeter.

The Emma Press
theemmapress.com
hello@theemmapress.com
Jewellery Quarter,
Birmingham, UK

Supported using public funding by
**ARTS COUNCIL
ENGLAND**

Contents

Stinky Banana

I know
if there's an unpeeled banana in the room
or a semi-peeled banana,
banana puree, banana bread
or banana milkshake.
I even know when someone
in my family has eaten a banana –
I can detect the scent on their skin
like a bloodhound.

I absolutely positively
hate bananas:
they are the worst fruit in the world.
I used to like the sweet taste
but the smell is enough
to make my stomach turn
and make my insides churn.
It's my body's way of saying,
'Get that thing away from me!'

I got really hungry the other day,
and there was nothing in the fridge
that I could readily eat except bananas.
I had to pinch my nose and then
gobble them down, ugh –
it was an awful moment.
I was holding my breath
the entire time,
eating it bit by bit.

I ate a banana to survive.
I think this is what pirates feel
when they are lost at sea for days
and don't have any sustenance.
They do what they need to do
to get through, including eating
the parrot on their shoulder
or someone's finger.

The Perfect Sneeze

My dad has a very loud sneeze.
His whole body shakes when he sneezes,
and it makes a loud, booming sound.

My mom's sneezes are small and squeaky:
she says *aachoo* and it sounds
unthreatening and cute.

My sister's sneezes are messy:
she gets covered in drool and then
rubs it all over her face.
It's quite gross.

On the other hand, my sneezes
are just perfect:
not too loud and not too squeaky,
not too drooly and not too dry.

Just the right combination
of sound, air and moisture.
They don't scare anybody,
not even the baby;
when I feel a sneeze coming on,
I don't have to warn anyone.
I don't fly up ten feet in the air –
it's just a normal-sounding sneeze
that is over very quickly.

Burps and Farts

Burps and farts are funny things
that involve gas.
I like both burps and farts
but I prefer to burp
when my tummy is full of air.

Burps smell like meals that I've eaten:
there's strawberry burps, omelette burps,
banana burps, vanilla custard burps
(those are actually quite delicious)
and even roast chicken burps.
It's a way to remember delicious food
after it's finished
and long digested in the intestines.

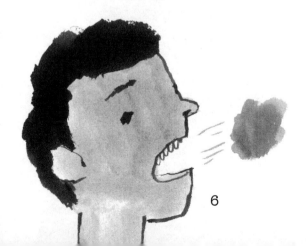

Farts, on the other hand, all smell the same,
like stinky methane
and that's a shame: there's no variety!
The only way to tell
one fart from the other
is through the sound it makes:
some are loud
like a rumbling volcano
while some are really soft,
like a whisper.

Rocks

I grew crystals in a plastic jar:
one was blue, one pink and one clear.
I was trying to make a salt lamp for my room.
Every day I would check on them
with my flashlight,
watch them grow in the chemical water.

First there was nothing,
then a tiny little stump,
then it grew into a bigger crystal:
an interesting shape
with lots of edges.
Every day it grew a bit more,
until all the water was gone
and in its place
was a perfect sharp-edged
crystal!

It's my dream to get real lava rock
fresh from the mouth of a volcano.
The closest I've come to lava rock
is in my mom's bathroom.
She had some earrings
with black lava rock in them
which my dad got for her from Iceland
(this was before I was born so I missed out).

I want to travel to Reykjavík,
which is the capital of Iceland.
Did you know that Iceland
is just a giant volcanic rock
that was formed after a volcano erupted?
If I could collect any rock for my rock collection
I would collect Iceland.
It would be the biggest rock in my collection –
an entire country!
But how would I move it in my car?
My car is a Toyota Corolla
and it is much smaller than an island.

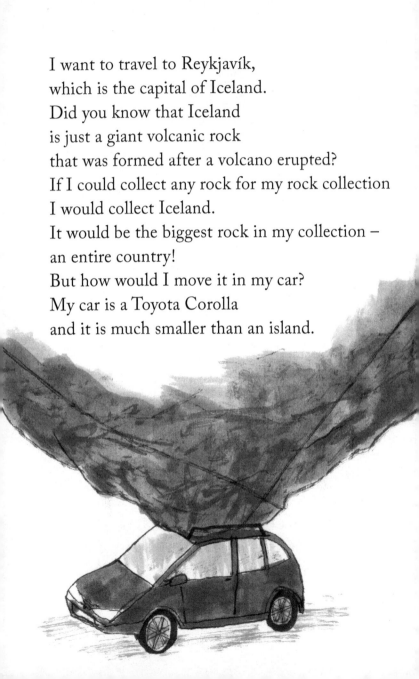

Time Outs

I get time outs
when I'm mean to my sister
when I push her
when I raise my voice
when I snatch a book from her hands
when I don't do my chores
or finish my vegetables

when I shout at my parents
and mimic them in the car
or when I don't act like a star
when I cry for no reason
and when I throw tantrums
in the supermarket
when I don't act my age
when I fly up in a rage
when I stomp on the grass

when I ruin the roses
when I spray my mom
with the water hose
even though she told me not to
when I don't put away my toys
when I touch my dad's laptop
without his permission
when I ignore the rules
and then it's time for consequences...
(I don't like consequences!
I like to get away with things and do
small naughty acts which go unnoticed.)

Once I ruined my mom's clothes –
I got acrylic paint on them
and it never washed out.
Once I didn't put my marbles away,
so my sister tried to eat one:
that was very 'dangerous'
and 'irresponsible' of me.
I fished it out with my finger,
but I was still given a time out.
A time out in my room is okay –
it's kind of fun.
A time out longer than ten minutes
is awful though, I'm done
with those.

Bedtime

At 8.30pm every day
I have a bath
and then it's time for bed,
shortly followed by
my least favourite moment of all time:
lying in bed! Yuck!

Why do I have to go to sleep?
Every single time
I'm awake under the covers and
my brain is giving me
fantastic ideas.
I want to do a million things!

My eyes are open,
my brain is saying:
let's build a sandcastle
let's watch television
let's play with the electric train
let's watch the stars
let's tickle your sister
let's sit at the computer
let's play videogames
let's read a book
let's watch a cartoon movie
let's watch Ironman 2
let's write big numbers
let's count coins
let's spoil a Sharpie
let's comb someone's hair
let's bake blueberry muffins
let's eat a raw tomato
let's run in circles
let's build a spaceship

My mind talks and talks
until it says:
let's close our eyes
just for one minute.
A short break
to think of more things.

And by some kind of magic
I wake up and it's the next day!

Moving to America

I told Juf Nathalie
that I was going to America.
She said, 'America?
You're going all the way to America?'
I said, 'Yes!'
I said it in Nederlands, not English.
She was speaking Nederlands too:
she said, 'Wanneer ga je naar Amerika?'
I don't remember what I said,
to be honest. I'm forgetting my Nederlands.
I want to learn it again,
but the words got lost
somewhere in my home.
Did we forget to bring them here?
Or are they hiding
in another room somewhere?

Hatchetfish

The hatchetfish and I
have one important thing in common:
we both
love shrimp.
It's so tasty and crunchy
and utterly delicious,
I buy it in bulk
from Costco.

I wonder if the hatchetfish
has a Costco membership
and rolls into the store with its cart,
flashes its membership card
to the lady at the entrance,
then heads to the freezers to load up on
ready-to-eat breaded shrimp.
Now that would be a sight!
I would definitely high-five
the hatchetfish.

Giant

I climbed a tree in the park
without any help.
My mom took a picture of me
high up on top –
I could see all the grownups
so small and timid down on the ground,
and their kids were the size of ants.

I felt like a giant, a thousand feet tall
with the superpower of infinite sight.
I was the king of the park:
I could see across
the beautiful blue California sky,
I could smell the sizzling barbecue,
I could almost taste everyone's picnic spread.
I could see beetles in the grass:
all things big, small, squishy,
round, dangerous and safe.

I was perfectly camouflaged
in the tree in my camouflage vest
and nobody, absolutely nobody
could see me.
It was the best: I could spy
on everyone with my binoculars
which let me see all the way
to the Diablo Hills
and the end of Crow Canyon Street.
It was quite the sight!

Intruder Drill
is Scary

In America
if you make a noise in class
someone can shoot you
so that's why you keep quiet.
It's very different from a fire drill –
for that you have to vacate the building
and run outside to the playground.
For an intruder drill
you can't go outside.

Ms Tam is in charge of keeping us safe –
she'll tie up the door with a strong rope.
My friend said, 'What if the intruder
has a sharp knife?'
Ms Tam said, 'The rope is hefty, so
it'll take a long time to cut through,
children – don't worry.
There's hope.
This will never happen, probably –
it's just in case of emergency
we have to practice this lunacy.
It's a dress rehearsal
for a horrible show.
Keep your tones low.'

I was trying to be quiet
but my friend kept talking.
I lay still on the rug:
I could hear my heart beating,
and my friend kept saying
what about
what about
what about
a trillion whatabouts.
a billion and ninety-nine whatabouts.

Fossils

I went to the San Diego Zoo
and saw the skeleton of
the mighty woolly mammoth,
which was amazing.
I saw fossils of extinct creatures
that used to live in Southern California
a thousand years ago.

I thought, there's probably a few fossils
hiding in my own backyard,
so I bought a dig kit and started digging
in the sandpit for bones.
I said to my dad,
'Baba, do you think
there are bones in our home
and fossils of ammonites,
brachiopods, corals
and trilobites?'

My dad thought for a long time
and then he said, 'What if you found
some chicken bones?'
I said, 'What? Chicken bones?!'
I laughed a lot.
Chicken bones are the tiniest
most disappointing
least interesting
bones in the world.

Bell Pepper

We thought we were growing green chillies.
We watered the jalapeño pepper plant and waited
for the spicy juices to run.
We were going to put them
in our chicken karahi
and make it extra spicy
so it burnt our mouths
as we ate.

One day I spotted three chillies
growing in the planter –
they were long and invitingly juicy.
I ran inside to tell everyone,
I shouted, 'The chillies are ripe,
the chillies are ripe!'
Then my mom stepped outside
with her culinary scissors
which I am not allowed to touch,
and she let me snip them one by one.

She told me not to taste,
but I couldn't help it –
I popped one in my mouth
and it wasn't spicy at all
because it was a bell pepper.

My mom said, 'Don't eat that!'
thinking it was a real chilli,
but I crunched it in my mouth
with a smile so she would think
I was the bravest jalapeño-eating
superhero in the world.

The Tooth Fairy
Makes Mistakes

One day my tooth fell out
and I put it under my pillow.
The tooth fairy left me money but
she didn't take my tooth (gasp!)
and she forgot it the night after that too.
She left me more money but kept
forgetting to take my tooth,
and she made this mistake
over and over again.

One day, the tooth fairy came too late
to give me money.
It was already 10am
and I thought maybe she was delayed
because she also needed to collect
other children's molars, incisors,
premolars and canines.

I would've waited till 9am,
but 10 is just too late.
I was waiting by the clock,
not having breakfast,
just watching the window
hoping for her to slip in,
pocket my tooth,
and leave that shiny dollar bill
in its usual place.
No room for more mistakes,
Ms Tooth!

Vanilla Vla

I like America more and more each day
but the thing I miss the most
about the Netherlands is
VLA
which is pronounced
FLA!

which is a creamy, tasty,
super delicious vanilla custard
that melts in your mouth.

I used to eat all the different types:
Slagroom Vla, Dubble Vla and
Chocolate Vla, yum!
Just thinking about it makes my mouth water
and my stomach growl.
I want it so bad.

My mom tried to make it for me,
strawberry custard out of a box,
but it was a disgusting pink colour
and didn't taste the same.
Then she looked up a recipe for vanilla custard
but it had eight eggs in it. Ew!
Real Vla had no eggs in it.
It was not eggyish at all.

Now my plan is to find a Dutch grocery store,
but I haven't been able to so far.
I just want someone to send me
three boxes of Vla –
I'll pay the shipping, the postage,
the everything.
Somebody send me a year's supply –
just do it now, please, I've told you why!

Bacteria

Why do we get sick? Because of bacteria.
It's possible to catch a flu and a fever –
but also, fish?
How does that work?
Washing hands is one way
to keep bacteria away,
because bacteria
are everywhere: in food, on our hands,
on the staircase, on our friends,
family, parents, plates…
Bacteria really don't discriminate!

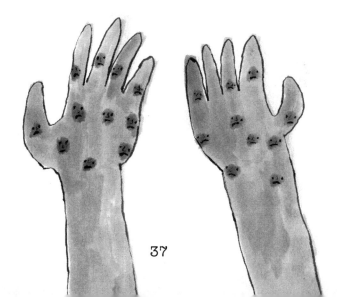

Last week my friend Gina
got a stomach flu: bacteria
were trying to tunnel into her stomach
and making her vomit.
Her snot turned green!
I think the bacteria won, that time.
But I think mostly
with human beings
bacteria keep winning,
right?

Flossing

School in the corona days
is not very fun,
but I like doing meetings
on Google Classroom and Zoom.

Today Mohib's internet
was not working and Mrs Banzet said
'Oh no Mohib, you're frozen!'
I thought she meant
he had turned into an ice cube
but he was still a human boy –
except his face was a mass of pixels,
dots and fuzzy outlines,
which wouldn't move at all,

Yesterday, Ryan's big brother
was flossing in the background.
Boy, did that get a laugh
out of Mrs Banzet!

I thought it was very weird and hilarious –
I like to floss in front of the mirror
but I am not as good as Ryan's brother yet.
I need to practice very hard during school.

The teacher says,
'Everybody look at your writing journals!'
but I can't stop thinking about
how cool flossing is.

First Grade

On the first day of first grade I felt scared,
because it was my first day,
but then I didn't feel nervous after that.

First grade is too easy!
I have to do easy peasy
lemon squeezy mathematics!
Like 1+1=2 and 2+2=4,
which is *so* simple.

I want to do multiplication!
I even learnt a few times tables
over the summer, for instance,
the one times table
and the two times table.

Wait! Before I forget,
I also want to tell you that I learnt
the five times table, the ten times
and the eleven times table –
those were the easy ones.
The four times table is sneaky –
it's hard to guess the numbers
just off the top of my head.

I wish I could be in school
with my friends, instead of on Zoom
with its boxes of fake children.
I would trade all the multiplication tables
in the world
to play with even one real kid.

School Attire

In my online class today,
someone showed up in underwear!
(I'm not going to say who,
because I'm not a tattle-tale.)

Everybody stared and laughed,
but at first the teacher didn't notice
that anything was amiss –
she was talking about Pete the Cat
and his white shoes,
and how many sight words
we learnt this week.
Then she went all quiet.

She said, 'I would just like to remind
everyone in class
to wear the appropriate school attire.'
I didn't understand many of the words she said,
but I could tell that this was about
not wearing clothes to school
and how *not okay*
that was.

Trees

Trees are natural storytellers,
because if you cut open the trunk of a tree
every circle tells a story of each year
of the tree's life.

It's not even necessary to cut a tree
to get to its story:
scientists use a special radar
to look at the rings inside the trunk,
which are like chapters in the book
of the tree.
A light side and a dark side in the trunk
equals one solar year.

If you count the rings
in a redwood tree
they might come to eight hundred,
because redwoods are
some of the oldest trees in the world.
I went to the Big Basin Redwood
    State Park
and saw trees that were five thousand
    years old –
that's a thousand times older than
    my grandmother
and she is really old!
The redwoods were one hundred and
    fifty metres tall.
(Now is the time to exclaim and say
    Wow!)

47

My Sister

enjoys putting a phone charger
round her neck.
Wouldn't you say
that's dangerous and strange?

She wears it like a necklace
and will scream loudly and cry
if you try to take it
away from her.

Maybe she thinks she needs
to be charged like a phone –
that's a funny thought for you to think about,
don't you agree?
Is that why she's always sleepy?
Because she has low battery?

Strawberry Guava

I thought the fruits
falling into my sand-pit
were ripe to eat.
They were small with leathery skin
and a strong strawberry smell,
but when I put one in my mouth
it tasted like raw fruit.

I ran inside to show my dad
and he was so surprised.
He googled it and said,
'These are strawberry guavas.
Where did you find them?'

I like to surprise people
with things I find outside,
like fossils, rocks or fruit.
'Outside,' I said, 'in our own yard.
You said this is not a fruit tree,
this is just a normal tree,
but you were wrong!
It's a guava tree and now it's putting out
delicious fruit except they're not
ready yet. Once they're fully ripe
we can eat them and
turn them into
yummy guava jam!'

Potty Breaks

My classes on Zoom are really long.
The thing that keeps me going
is when, on occasion,
Matt S or Matt M
or Matt L (there's many Matts in my class)
says: 'Mrs Banzet I need to go potty'
or 'Mrs B, I need to go to the toilet.'

Or, if they are being very polite, they say:
'May I please be excused to use the bathroom?'
This makes me laugh really loudly –
I'm so glad I'm on mute
because I don't want my teacher
to know just how funny
the thought of other people pooping is.

Squirrels

Squirrels are furry little bandits
who steal my apples and apricots!
They hide in the tree
but their bushy tails give them away.
They try to be cool and covert
like James Bond
but actually they're Captain Obvious.

I call the squirrel in my yard Guffy.
She loves nibbling the mulberries,
holding one in both her hands
like a small hairy person.
When I tried to stop her
she got startled, did a crazy somersault
and landed on my solar lamp!

My dad said, 'What the heck?'
And then I said, 'What the heck?'
And then my dad said,
'Don't say what the heck.
That's a rude word.'

Guffy was watching us
through her dark, black eyes,
still covered in the fruity spoils of our backyard
from head to tail, but she did not show
a morsel of guilt.

Dystopia

The Parent Teacher Association at my school
is having a fun run on Zoom.
I used to like in-person fun runs
but I'm very unsure about what
a fun run on Zoom entails.

My mom said, 'Does this mean
you have to run in place in the living room
while standing in front of the computer?
That's dystopian!'

This means it will be an awful lot
like Mr Gonzalez's physical education class,
where we have to do lunges and jumping jacks
in front of the computer.

Sometimes there's twenty-four kids
frozen in place while doing yoga stretches
or running animal laps in their kitchen
with sleepy parents
in silly pyjamas
in the background.

Propaganda

We end each day in online school
with a song that goes like this:

'We had a good day,
we had a great day,
let's go back home.

We had a good day,
we had a fun day,
let's go back home.'

I want to re-write the song
so that it's more honest:

'We had an average day,
we had an okay day,
we were sitting on a chair
for six hours.

I want to go back to school,
I want to play in the playground,
it was a strange day, it was a sweaty day,
with twenty technical glitches,
seventy cases of slow internet, and
twenty-seven instances
of the blue screen of death.'

We have to have school spirit,
wear spirit wear and shout *Go Falcons!*
I feel my head is smushy
and I don't want to sing happy songs.

My mom says that musical lyrics
that are untrue
are called propaganda.
That is extremely true.

Self-driving Car

I was on the highway
when I saw a car without a driver.
It was thrilling!
I had read a book about
self-driving cars a day earlier,
and now I was seeing one
in real life.
I said to my dad,
'I see a self-driving machine.'

But he said, 'Maybe the driver
is just really short.'
I said, 'WHAT?!
How could the driver be that small?
Then he would probably be a child
like me.'

My dad said, 'Okay fine,
maybe you are right.'
I said, 'Maybe?
Don't say MAYBE!
You should say
OF COURSE!'

Yosemite

We rented a cabin
when we went to Yosemite National Park.
It was really lush and beautiful
and we went hiking in the forest every day,
but what I really wanted to do
the entire time we were there
was climb one of the rock formations,
but I was too scared
to scale the giant rocks.

I saw a man all the way at the top –
he was wearing a safety harness
and looked really focused,
like he was solving
the most difficult algebra problem.
He put one hand over the other
and scaled the mountain,
getting closer
and closer
to the sun.

65

While we were down there in the valley
roasting marshmallows
and telling spooky stories,
the rock-climbers were up in the air,
close to the cumulous clouds,
directly under the stars,
watching us with a bird's eye:
kings of the rocks, masters of Yosemite.

Bees

At first I was really scared of bees
especially after my close encounter with one,
when a big juicy bee came into my living room
and got trapped in the curtain.
We had to pry it out
and release it back into the wild.
Since then I have been very afraid
of bees biting me,
but Mama told me that only scared bees
attack human beings
and I was scared of a creature
who was scared of me –
that was so silly, right?

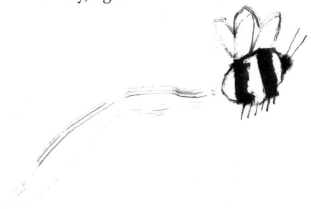

In fact, she said, most bees are harmless
and only interested in drinking
flower juice – nectar –
and making honey.
She said most bees in California
are probably really thirsty during the drought,
so we should put out a jug of water for them.

I said, 'Mama, a jug is not safe
because bees can fall in and drown in them.
My research tells me that actually a shallow tray
with water and wet rocks is the best thing for them,
because they can stand in it and drink water safely.'
HA! One point for me
and none for Mama.

Watermelon Hat

Eating watermelon in the summer
helps to quench my thirst,
and that's not all:
I use the watermelon peel
as a hat for my sister and me.
It keeps our heads really cool and wet,
and we pretend to be soldiers in a war!
Superheroes fighting bad guys
with our fruity armour.
We beat the heat
with our 'cool' headgear.

I wanted to go to bed
wearing my watermelon hat,
so that I wouldn't get hot
under the covers,
but my mom said no.
She rejects all my fun plans –
adults love the word 'no'.
But what about watermelon underwear?
Now there's an idea
which is hard to strike down.

The Dentist

My dentist's office looks like a giant ship,
and everyone wears scrubs
with pirates on them.
At reception, there's a treasure chest
where I can pick out a toy once I'm done
with all the messy business
of having clean teeth.
(At least, there used to be one.
They got it rid of it
because of the sticky, icky virus.)

Last time I went in
they gave me laughing gas,
which didn't make me laugh at all.
It just made me very sleepy,
so I wanted to close my eyes
and dream about riding the waves
while feeling the ship rock from side to side.

But instead someone in a mask
was poking around in my teeth
and complaining about
my 'overactive gag reflex'.

They kept talking to each other,
as if I wasn't even in the room.
I'm right here, I wanted to say.
Your scalpel is in my mouth, lady!

They replaced my cavities with fillings
and covered my teeth
with sealants to form
an insurmountable barrier against bacteria
so you could say that my mouth is now invincible.
After that, I got a balloon
shaped like a pumpkin
and my head felt all wobbly like the balloon.

Dandelions

Dandelion are great travellers
because they can float in the sky.
They go from country to country
and never have to walk
or take the aeroplane:
they can fly up high in the sky
on feathery filaments
and air.

I think dandelions
don't even need to pack a suitcase
and they don't need a passport
or a ticket –
all they need to do is
catch a good breeze
and off they go,
up up up!

If they wanted,
they could even reach space
and be in zero gravity
until they got
sucked into a black hole,
uh-oh.

Beards

I don't want to have a beard.
It's my worst nightmare
to have poky hair follicles
sticking out from my chin.
It's going to be a very sad day
when I grow hair from my face.

My dad has a beard
and it tickles my cheeks
when I snuggle with him.
He likes to shave his beard
and his face gets white and foamy
before becoming
smooth and hairless.

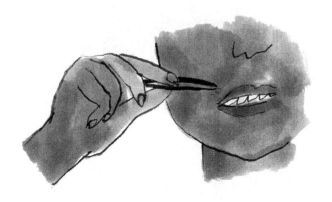

My mom also has a small beard,
but you can barely see it.
She pretends that it's not even there,
and she pulls out stray hairs with tweezers
which is very satisfying to watch.

When I tell her, 'Mama, you have a beard,'
she gets very embarrassed and says, 'No, I don't,'
before disappearing into the loo to pluck out
some of her rogue beard hairs.

I wonder why she is so secretive about it.
I don't like beards, but I think my mom
hates them even more than I do.
She looks at them in a magnifying mirror
which makes her hairs and pores look huge.

Her beard is her secret shame
so don't tell her I told you –
she would be so mad!

Poop

A poop is something your body makes
once you've digested your food,
and there are many different types.
Like volcano poop, polar bear poop,
asteroid poop, also book poop –
a poop that is shaped like this book.
Isn't that funny?
Elephant poop is shaped like
(you guessed it)
like an E-L-E-P-H-A-N-T.

One day I was mightily constipated
and my mama said,
'Let's feed you prunes,
massage your tummy and give you
a warm bath.'
Halfway through the shower
I said, 'I NEED TO POOP!'
and out came one volcano poop,
one pickle poop,
five ball poops,
one rock poop,
one telescope poop,
and one tiger poop.

I took one last look
at all the treasures in the bowl,
then pressed the button
and away it went.
I was very sad to lose
all my hard work.

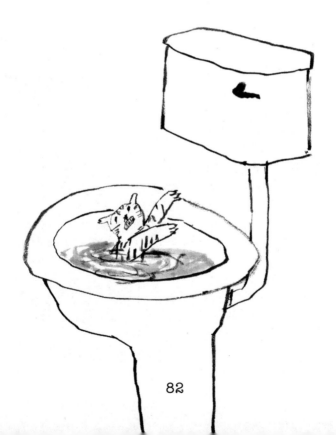

Aphids

We spent a million days
growing tomatoes,
watering them daily,
tying the vines to the tomato cage,
until finally we had a dozen
beautiful red cherry tomatoes.
But alas! it took only two days
for the entire plant to be destroyed
by evil, scheming aphids
with big hungry bellies.

My produce dreams went out in a flash
when the leaves sprouted a strange rash
one morning
and I spotted a host of bugs in the planter.
It was time to get set things right:
it was time
for insecticide.

We sprayed the plant
and soon we were rid of them,
but the holes remained.
Now I know it takes ages
to nurture something,
tame it, grow it,
and it only takes a few hours
for insects to chomp it
to absolute nothingness.

Frustration

Sometimes
I try to remember
the word
for the sad feeling I have
when I wake up in the morning,
or the word for
how I feel when my sister
tears my books,
or the word
for the warm feeling I get
when my mom hugs me
really tight
at night
before tucking me into bed
and switching off the lights.

There are so many words
I don't know –
and there are some words
I do know
that I can't remember,
like the words 'camouflage'
or 'imagination'
or 'pandemonium',
because my brain
won't tell me.

I keep asking it,
'What is the right word
and how do you spell it?'
and my brain replies,
'I DONT KNOW.'
That's very 'frustrating'.

Nothing

What does nothing look like?
What is there when there is nothing?
What was there before the Earth,
before the Big Bang,
when there was nothing on the Earth?
No trees, no sky, no roads, no dirt –
when there were no human beings,
no sky, no clouds, no colour?
What was there?

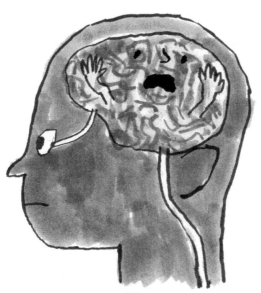

The Yellow Sky

I woke up this morning
to find that the sky
was a strange, smoky colour.
I thought, 'What?
Is there going to be
acid rain?'
But I found out
that the colour of the sky
is because of the wildfires
in California.
There is ash
all over my plants,
the forest, and even
the entire universe.

It looks like it's night-time,
but it's not even lunchtime:
it's 11am in the morning!
The colour yellow
is making me feel sad.
My walls
are bathed
in an eerie light
which most things
look yellow in,
such as the ceiling,
my feet, and even Mama's teeth!

My Best Friend

I can't see my best friend nowadays
because of Covid-19
but I can talk to her
whenever I want
and I see a picture of us
on a playdate in my mind.

My best friend's name is Gina
and she is the bravest girl I know.
She can turn cartwheels across the room
and do a handstand too,
so that's a double bonus.

One day a bully was bullying me,
and Gina got really mad at him.
She scrunched up her nose
and said, 'BACK OFF.'
Then she had a clever idea:
she turned to me and said,
'Let's tell him if he stops
he won't be in any trouble,
but then let's tell on him anyway.'

This was our secret.
It's difficult to keep secrets usually,
as they twist and turn inside of us,
wanting to come out and be revealed,
but it is surprisingly easy
to keep secrets from mean bullies.

Gina told the teacher the entire incident
and the bully had to stand up
in front of the entire class
and 'explain his behaviour.'
He got very embarrassed and hot in the face;
that's what happens
when you are a nasty turd in school.

The Big Dig

The other day I was digging
for gems, rubies
and possibly
a treasure chest.

I made a big hole in the gravel
which I was very proud of:
it was the biggest hole
that I had ever made.
It was the size of a crater,
and it was the closest
I had ever come
to the Earth's molten core.

I kept digging and digging
as I wanted to find at least
one precious stone,
but then the sun went down
and my mom said, 'Come inside.'

I will start again tomorrow.
If I go with the flow,
just think of all the things I will find!
Velociraptor bones, crystals,
stalagmites, buried cities...

I just need to make sure
I spend all my free time digging.
It will take a lot of hard work
finding hidden structures in the dirt,
so I will probably have strong muscles
and be a grownup by the time it's over,
wouldn't you agree?

NOW WRITE YOUR OWN POEM!

Here are some ideas to get you started...

What is the **bravest thing** you've ever done?
Imagine you're standing in front of a big crowd
of people at a party, and write a poem with
what you would say to them, to impress them
with your grand feat. Remember to explain *why*
it was so brave, and how you felt while doing it!

What is your **favourite food**? Why you
like it so much? Does this food come
in different varieties, like the Vla on
page 34? Write a poem in praise of
your favourite food, describing what it looks
like, what it tastes like, and why it's the best.

In 2020, the Covid-19 pandemic began and
we all had to make some changes in our lives.
What changed in your life? Is there anything
you used to be able to do that you had to stop
doing? What did you have to *start* doing,
because of the pandemic? Write two lists,
starting like this:

Before the pandemic, I could...

When the pandemic began, we all had to...

A lot of children had to start doing online school in 2020. What did you think of online school? Did things ever go wrong? **Write a new school song**, like on page 59, describing what online school was really like. If you were already homeschooled to begin with, write a homeschool song!

What is the **most fun game you know**? Imagine an alien has landed on Earth and you are trying to explain to them how to play. Start by outlining what the rules are, and then explain why this game is so fun.

Write a poem about **your best friend**, or your favourite person. Why do you like them? What do you do together? How did you meet?

ABOUT THE AUTHORS

Rakhshan Rizwan is a writer and scholar working at the intersection of creative and scholarly practice.

She is a postdoctoral researcher affiliated with Utrecht University in the Netherlands and has a PhD in Comparative Literature. She is the winner of the 2015 Judith Khan Memorial Prize for Poetry.

Her debut pamphlet, *Paisley* (The Emma Press, 2017), was shortlisted for the Saboteur Award and the Michael Marks Award. Her poems have appeared in *Nimrod, Blue Lyra Review, Bird's Thumb, aaduna* and *Postcolonial Text*.

She is the author of *Kashmiri Life Narratives* (Routledge, 2020), a research monograph which explores the intersections between human rights and literature in the Valley of Kashmir.

She speaks four languages and is originally from Pakistan but has lived in Germany, the Netherlands and currently lives in the Bay Area in the United States.

Yusuf Samee is 6 years old. He is a first-grade student at Twin Creeks Elementary School.

He likes collecting rocks and leaves, growing vegetables, and playing with numbers in his mind.

He was born in the city of Delft in The Netherlands and now lives in the Bay Area in California.

ABOUT THE ILLUSTRATOR

Benjamin Phillips is an artist and illustrator based in Hastings. From his studio by the sea he creates ceramics, paintings and illustrative work.

Benjamin enjoys drawing, dogs and a cold beverage. Sometimes all at the same time.

benjaminphillips.co.uk

ABOUT THE EMMA PRESS

The Emma Press is an independent publishing house based in the Jewellery Quarter, Birmingham, UK. It was founded in 2012 by Emma Dai'an Wright, and specialises in poetry, short fiction and children's books.

In 2020 The Emma Press received funding from Arts Council England's Elevate programme, developed to enhance the diversity of the arts and cultural sector by strengthening the resilience of diverse-led organisations.

You can find out more about the Emma Press and buy books here:

theemmapress.com
Facebook @theemmapress
Twitter: @theemmapress
Instagram: @theemmapress

SUPER GUPPY

Poems by Edward van de Vendel
Illustrated by Fleur van de Weel
Translated from Dutch by David Colmer

Have you ever had a pet? Or have you ever
stopped to look at all of the small things in
your home that make up your life? From
wet socks to being tucked into bed at night,
and strongly featuring one inspiring guppy
fish with real staying power – *Super Guppy*
stays close to home, but it's a home full of
fun, jokes, and surprising adventure.

Paperback ISBN 978-1-910139-65-3
Poems aimed at children aged 8+

MOON JUICE

Poems by Kate Wakeling
Illustrated by Elīna Brasliņa

Meet Skig, who's meant to be a warrior
(but is really more of a worrier). Meet a
giddy comet, skidding across the sky with
her tail on fire. Put a marvellous new
machine in your pocket and maybe you'll
be able to fix all your life's problems.

*Winner of the 2017 CLiPPA, the Centre of
Literacy in Primary Education's award for
children's poetry books*

Paperback ISBN 978-1-910139-49-3
Poems aimed at children aged 8+